The Green Prophet

Written and illustrated
by Nelson Seda

Once upon a time, in a city not too far away, called Muddville, there lived a small green frog by the name of Russ.

Russ was sitting on a lily pad in the pond outside the city with some of his friends. This was on the second day of the week in the month of the flies, this very year.

Suddenly, he heard a voice that seemed to come from the air

surrounding him. Not a loud voice, but a warm and peaceful voice telling him something wonderful...something that he must share with the people of Muddville.

So, he hopped out of the pond and onto the land, making his way to the city of Muddville. After hopping along the road for two days, he stopped at a farm about a mile from the city.

There he met a farmer by the name of Ron. Russ said to Farmer Ron, "Hello there, RRRRIBBITT. Is there, by chance, any way you can help me get to the city of Muddville, RRRRIBBITT?" Farmer Ron looked all around to find out where the voice was coming from. "Who...who said that?"

As he looked around, all he could see was a small green frog sitting by the side of the road.

Farmer Ron shook his head saying, "I must be going crazy. I'm hearing things now." Then he shouted loudly, "Is anyone out there?"

Russ, the small green frog said, "RRRRIBBITT, down here.

I'm down here! And, I have something wonderful to share with you RRRRIBBITT!"

When he heard the frog speak, Farmer Ron fell over in surprise.

Then Russ the frog hopped onto Farmer Ron's chest and began to tell him the wonderful news that he had heard from God.

After hearing everything that Russ the frog had to tell him, Farmer Ron got up. Then he picked up Russ and carried him all the way to the city of Muddville.

When they finally got to the city, they found themselves in front of a church building.

There they met the pastor whose name was Phil. When he saw Russ the frog in Farmer Ron's hand, Pastor Phil said, "Hello and God bless you! Is there a special reason why you're carrying a frog?"

Farmer Ron smiled and said, "In this case there is." Pastor Phil listened as the farmer told him the wonderful news that Russ the frog had shared with him. Pastor Phil began to laugh in disbelief.

Then Russ finally spoke up and said to Pastor Phil, "RRRRIBBITT, it was funny to me at first, too. But, after I

realized that God had spoken to me, I had to share it with you too, RRRRIBBITT."

Pastor Phil looked at the talking frog, and fell over just like Farmer Ron had done. He had never seen or heard of such a thing before in his life! So Farmer Ron and Russ the frog helped Pastor Phil get used to the idea of a talking frog. After Pastor Phil began to feel better, they all went to City Hall to see Mayor Tom.

When he first heard Russ the frog speak to him, Mayor Tom also fell over. Then, when he heard the wonderful news that Russ the frog had to share, he decided to call a town meeting. All the people of Muddville were invited.

All the people came to City Hall to hear what Mayor Tom
had to say. When Mayor Tom explained the wonderful news,
they found it very hard to believe him. They began to shout,
and some of them even laughed at poor Mayor Tom.

But Mayor Tom said, "Well, if you don't believe me, then hear
it for yourselves from the one who told me." He turned to one
side and called out, "Russ, will you please come out here and
tell the good people of Muddville what you have heard from
God and shared with me?"

The people looked all around to see who the Mayor was talking to. They were all very surprised to see a small green frog hop onto the stage. The people of Muddville began to laugh even more. Russ the frog hopped past Mayor Tom and up to the microphone. Everyone waited to see what would happen next.

Mayor Tom said, "Quiet down and give Russ the frog a chance to speak." Then everyone laughed even louder.

Russ the frog took a deep breath and began to talk to the people. "RRRRIBBITT, RRRRIBBITT. I heard the voice of God tell me how much He cares for all the people in Muddville, RRRRIBBITT.

"God loves you and wants to bless all of you. The first thing He wants to do is change the name of the city of Muddville. RRRRIBBITT, He wants to give the city a name that will help you know His love for you."

When they heard Russ speaking to them, all the people were very surprised. Some of them fell over just like the others had done. But, some of them were amazed that God cared enough about them, to send them a talking frog.

Then Mr. Wilson, the banker, started to wave his hands in the air and shout loudly for all to hear. "Why should we believe *you*? How do we know for sure it was God who spoke to you? What will happen to us if we *don't* change the city's name? I want an answer before we make any changes around here."

Everyone agreed with Banker Wilson and began to shout at Russ the frog. Russ said, "Well, RRRRIBBITT, how many frogs are there who can tell you that God wants to bless you? If you don't want to change the name of the city to the one that God has for you, then you won't receive the blessing, RRRRIBBITT. Remember, the blessing is in the name. No new name, no blessing."

Then Mayor Tom stepped up to the microphone and said, "I want to say this in all fairness to Russ the frog. He hopped a very long way to let us know that God is thinking about us. We really should give him an answer before he goes back home."

Pastor Phil stood up and said, "I think we should pray before deciding on anything. If we pray, the Holy Spirit will show us what to do. For the Word of God says that the Holy Spirit is the Spirit of truth." They all agreed and bowed their heads to pray, while they held each other's hands.

When they finished praying, Farmer Ron said, "I think we should hear the new name for the city and then decide." Russ the frog said, "RRRRIBBITT, why is this so hard to understand?

God wants to bless you. But, if it will help you all to decide, I'll tell you the new name God has for the city. Remember, in the new name there will be a blessing.

"God wants the city of Muddville to change its name to 'FOREVER GLADNESS.' Those who live in the city of FOREVER GLADNESS will be blessed and receive peace and joy forevermore." Russ the frog stopped and looked at everyone with tears in his eyes. With a deep breath, the small green frog said, "If you do not change the name of the city, everything will stay the same. Everyone will live their lives day by day trying to make blessings happen. But again I say, no name change, no blessing."

When they heard the new name and the blessings God had promised, they knew that God truly loved them. That very day they changed the name of the city to FOREVER GLADNESS and the people *were* truly blessed. They sang songs of joy and danced in the streets. Everyone was happy, except for Mr. Wilson the banker. So, he moved to a small town called Discourageville where he lives an unhappy life, always asking himself why he missed the blessing.

As for the small green frog named Russ, he went back to the

pond and never spoke a word to anyone again. But, they say late at night, on the fourth day of the week in the month of the shooting stars, you can hear someone singing sweet songs of praise to God from the center of the pond. There sits a group of small green frogs looking up toward the heavens.

Do you believe that God can use you to make a difference in *your* city, so that He can bless it too? RRRRIBBITT, I do, RRRRIBBITT.

THE END

GOD WANTS TO BLESS YOU

Many are looking for God's blessing but cannot find it. One blessing God wants to give you is His Son Jesus Christ. By saying this prayer you can receive Jesus Christ into your heart and be blessed forever.

Father God, I ask to be forgiven for all my sins and I turn away from them. I want to receive Your Son Jesus Christ into my heart now, as my Lord and Savior forever. Thank You for Your blessing. Amen.